Eric Knight's

LASSIE COME-HOME

Student Guide

 MEMORIA PRESS

MEMORIA PRESS

www.MemoriaPress.com

Eric Knight's
LASSIE COME-HOME

STUDENT GUIDE

Contributing Editors: Brett Vaden, Laura Bateman, and Leigh Lowe

ISBN 978-1-61538-056-5

First Edition © 2010 Memoria Press | 0419

Cover illustration by Starr Steinbach

Contents

Teaching Guidelines

PREPARING TO READ:

Review

- Orally review any previous vocabulary.
- Review the plot of the book as read so far.
- Periodically review the concepts of character, setting, and plot.

Study Guide Preview

- Reading Notes:
    - Read aloud together.
    - This section gives the students key characters, places, and terms that are relevant to a particular time period, etc.
- Vocabulary:
    - Read aloud together so that students will recognize words when they come across them in their reading.
- Comprehension Questions:
    - Read through these questions with students to encourage purposeful reading.

READING:

- Student reads the chapter (or selection of the chapter for that lesson) independently or to the teacher (for younger students).
- For younger students, you can alternate between teacher-read and student-read passages. Model good reading skills. Encourage students to read expressively and smoothly. Teacher may occasionally take oral reading grades.
- While reading, mark each vocabulary word as you come across it.
- Have students take note in their study guide margin of pages where a comprehension question is answered.

AFTER READING:

Vocabulary

- Look at each word within the context that it is used, and help your students come up with the best synonym that defines the word. (Make sure students know the meaning of the synonym.)
- Record the word's meaning in the students' study guides. (Use students' knowledge of Latin and other vocabulary to decipher meanings.)

Comprehension Questions

- Older students can answer these questions independently, but younger students (2nd-4th) need to answer the questions orally, form a good sentence, and then write it down, using correct punctuation, capitalization, and spelling. (You may want to write the sentence down for younger students after forming it orally, and then let students copy it perfectly.)
- It is not necessary to write the answer to every question. Some may be better answered orally.
- Answering questions and composing answers is a valuable learning activity. Questions require students to think; writing a concise answer is a good composition exercise.

Quotations and Discussion Questions

- Use the Quotations and Discussion Questions section of each lesson as a guide to your oral discussion of the key concepts in the chapter that may not be covered in the comprehension questions.
- These talking points can take your oral discussion to a higher level than covered in the students' written work. Use this time as an opportunity to introduce higher-level thinking. You can introduce concepts the students may not be mature enough to fully understand yet but that would be beneficial for them to begin thinking about.
- A key to the Discussion Questions is in the back of the Teacher Guide.

Enrichment

- The Enrichment activities include composition, copywork, dictation, research, mapping, drawing, poetry work, literary terms, and more.
- This section has a variety of activities in it, but the most valuable activity is composition. Your students should complete at least one composition assignment each week. Proof students' work and have students copy composition until grammatically perfect. Insist on clear, concise writing. For younger students, start with 2-3 sentences, and do the assignment together. The students can form good sentences orally as you write them down, and then the students copy them.
- These activities can be completed as time and interest allow. Do not feel you need to complete all of these activities. Choose the ones that you feel are the best use of your students' time.

Unit Review and Tests

- There is a unit review and a quiz or test following every few lessons (varies by individual guide).
- On the weeks that have these reviews and tests, you may want to do the review early in the week, and then drill it orally a couple of times before giving the test at the end of the week.
- A final comprehensive test is also included.

Reading Notes

moorlands	hill land where only certain plants can grow
dog fancier	dog lover
harum-scarum	reckless
kennelmen	person who tends a kennel or dog house

Vocabulary: Write the meaning of each bold word or phrase.

1. In that **bleak** part of northern England_____

2. the dog seems to **thrive** _____

3. walking at the heels of humbly **clad** workmen_____

4. **bludgeoned** by fate _____

Setting and Characters: Identify each character and place.

1. Sam Carraclough_____

_____

2. Joe_____

_____

3. Lassie _____

_____

4. Mother _____

_____

5. The Duke of Rudling _____

_____

6. Greenall Bridge _____

_____

7. Yorkshire _____

_____

Comprehension Questions: Answer the following in complete sentences.

1. What is the first reason Lassie is the best-known dog in the village?

   _____

   _____

2. Of all places in the world, the dog is _____ in the county of _____.

3. Why does the dog thrive in this particular place?

   _____

   _____

4. What do the women of the village say about Lassie that is the second reason Lassie is the best-known dog in the village?

   _____

5. What is the third reason Lassie is the best-known dog in Greenall Bridge?

   _____

   _____

6. What kind of work do the men in the hundreds of Yorkshire villages do?

   _____

7. What is the irony in the picture of poor village miners followed by their collies?

   _____

   _____

Enrichment

1. Look at the publication page. What is the original publication date of *Lassie Come-Home*? What major events were happening around this time?
2. Read the Biographical Sketch of the author in the Appendix, and write a one-paragraph summary of his life.

   _____

   _____

   _____

   _____

   _____

   _____

   _____

Reading Notes

dole	government payment to people without work
collier	coal miner
poor times	times of need and lack of provisions or money

Vocabulary: Write the meaning of each bold word or phrase.

1. No one seemed afraid that something **dire** had happened _____

2. Almost automatically, by a habit **ingrained** _____

3. It did not mean **luxurious** living for them _____

4. he turned back to the fire and stared into it **intently** _____

Comprehension Questions: Answer the following in complete sentences.

1. What is different when Joe comes out of school that has never happened before?

   _____

   _____

2. What is the irony of humans always being "five minutes late" and animals always being on time?

   _____

   _____

3. How do Joe's mother and the village people cover up their hurts and disappointments?

   _____

   _____

4. Why has Lassie not kept her appointment as she always has before?

   _____

   _____

5. Contrast the behavior of Joe's mother and father when Joe says Lassie is gone. Who tells Joe the sad news?

   _____

   _____

   _____

   _____

Quotations

1. *Joe Carraclough solved his problem as hundreds of thousands of boys solve their problems the world over. He ran home to tell his mother.*

2. *He knew that his father no longer went to work. He knew, too, that his father and mother never spoke of it before him—that in their rough, kind way they had tried to keep their burdens of living from bearing also on his young shoulders*

Discussion Questions

1. Why does Sam storm out of the cottage?
2. The author tells us that although Joe understands the reasons Lassie has to be sold, "his heart still cried for Lassie." What does this mean?

Enrichment

1. Yorkshire county was once filled with hundreds of small mining villages. What did the men in these villages mine, and what was the name of the mine in Greenall Bridge? What was life like for these mining families? How had Sam Carraclough been bludgeoned by fate? Read about the Industrial Revolution in the Appendix.
2. For more information and pictures describing the Industrial Revolution, check out this book: *Industrial Revolution*, edited by John D. Clare. Gulliver Books: New York, 1994.
3. Copy or write from dictation the third paragraph in the chapter.

Reading Notes

rhododendron	flowering bush
Ridlings of Yorkshire	three counties that once made up Yorkshire
King's English	a respected English accent
caveat emptor	Latin phrase meaning "let the buyer beware"

Vocabulary: Write the meaning of each bold word or phrase.

1. He turned with bristling **moustaches** _____

2. this drawback is absolutely **imperceptible** _____

3. There was … a growing desire that was at first **vague**. _____

Comprehension Questions: Answer the following in complete sentences.

1. Identify any new characters.

   _____

   _____

2. What is the Duke's reputation?

   _____

   _____

3. Why does the Duke believe that the world is going "to pot"?

   _____

   _____

4. How long does it take the Duke to get Lassie, and how does he finally get her?

   _____

   _____

5. What is coping?

   _____

   _____

6. What is Lassie's time sense telling her?

   _____

   _____

Quotations

Horses could not run so fast, young men were not so brave and dashing, women were not so pretty, flowers did not grow so well, and as for dogs, if there were any decent ones left in the world, it was because they were in his own kennels.

Discussion Questions

1. Why does the Duke like Priscilla despite her pertness with him?
2. Describe Hynes; how is his speech different, and why does it fit his character?
3. Why is the Duke disappointed?

Enrichment

1. Yorkshire is one of many counties in England. Look at the map of England and its counties in the Appendix. Observe and count the counties of England, and then, using an encyclopedia or online map resource, label the counties. Color Yorkshire. While Scotland and Wales are part of the country called the United Kingdom, they are also considered countries in themselves, so color them gray so that they are set apart from England.

2. Write a character sketch of the Duke of Rudling describing his personality, dress, unusual mannerisms, etc.

_____

_____

_____

_____

_____

_____

_____

_____

_____

_____

_____

3. On a separate sheet of paper, draw a picture of the Duke using the character sketch you wrote for composition. Try to include everything the author told you about him (e.g., his black hawthorne stick).

Reading Notes

muzzle   nose and mouth of a dog

linseed   seed of the flax plant

Vocabulary: Write the meaning of each bold word or phrase.

1. He stood for a moment, and then his voice rang **shrill**. _____

2. one that was eloquent of **exasperation** _____

3. his greatest dream and **ambition** _____

4. "I were just cleaning her up a bit," he said **ponderously** _____

Comprehension Questions: Answer the following in complete sentences.

1. Describe Joe's reaction to seeing Lassie after school. How is Joe different once he understands that Lassie has escaped?

    _____

    _____

2. How does Joe try to persuade his parents to let Lassie stay?

    _____

    _____

    _____

3. What does Mrs. Carraclough eventually do for Lassie? Mr. Carraclough?

    _____

    _____

    _____

    _____

    _____

4. Why does Sam get angry at Hynes?

    _____

    _____

    _____

    _____

Quotations

He took the brush and cloth from his son and, kneeling on the rug, began working expertly on the dog's coat, rubbing the rich, deep coat with the cloth, cradling the aristocratic muzzle carefully in one hand, while with the other he worked over the snow white of the collie's ruff and artistically fluffed out the "leggings" and the "apron" and the "petticoats."

Discussion Questions

1. Read the paragraph that begins with, "My goodness, sometimes it seems to me that the men i' this village think more o' their tykes than they do o' their flesh and blood." Why do you think the author then tells us that "Joe's father shifted his feet uneasily"?
2. Find two ways Joe mimics his father in the chapter.
3. What kind of dog does Hynes call Lassie? Why is this significant?

Enrichment

1. Accents, or the ways people speak in different parts of a country, often appear in our story. Joe speaks in the long Yorkshire accent to the men at the Labor Exchange, and Hynes uses the nasal, clipped accent of Southern England. In the two passages below, find the words that show the accents, and write what they mean.

   "Ye wouldn't have me takking her back lewking like a mucky Monday wash, would'ta?"

   "Ow, Hi thought so," he cried. "Hi just thought as 'ow Hi'd find 'er 'ere."

2. Copy or write from dictation the paragraph that follows these words from Joe: "Lassie's come home."

   _____

   _____

   _____

   _____

   _____

   _____

   _____

   _____

   _____

   _____

   _____

Reading Notes

tryst	meeting, appointment
servile	slavish or submissive
plaguing	troublesome or annoying
hobnailed	having nailed-in soles on a shoe or boot

Vocabulary: Write the meaning of each bold word or phrase.

1. They would **relent** and let her stay with them _____

2. The words **cascaded** over Joe. _____

3. she walked in and went to her **accustomed** place _____

4. the **menacing** advance of her grandfather. _____

Comprehension Questions: Answer the following in complete sentences.

1. Compare and contrast Joe's interaction with his parents this second time.

   _____

   _____

   _____

2. What is their solution to stop Lassie from escaping?

   _____

3. How do we see virtue in Sam's character from his conversation with the Duke?

   _____

   _____

4. Contrast the way Priscilla sees the Carracloughs with the way the Duke and Hynes see them.

   _____

   _____

   _____

   _____

5. What about Lassie's actions reveals that she has not taken to her new home?

   _____

   _____

Discussion Questions

1. This chapter has some moments of humor and some of seriousness. What are some examples?
2. What do you predict will happen next in the story? Why?

Enrichment

1. The county of Yorkshire is a place of moorlands, which have appeared in many other stories, such as *All Creatures Great and Small*, *The Hound of the Baskervilles*, *The Secret Garden*, and *Wuthering Heights*. The next chapter will talk about the moors, so read the description of moorlands below, and then draw a picture of what you imagine they look like.

   Moorland or moor is an area of hilly land without trees and without farming. These hills roll over the countryside, above the little cottages, villages, and rock-walled pastureland. They are known for frequent rainfall. Because the soil is not very absorbent, water tends to flow quickly down the hills to streams, or it collects in bogs connected to and intermingling with the moors. Only certain kinds of vegetation, like tall purple heather and bracken (large, rough ferns), can grow on moorland. These plants have to be cut back now and again because of their tendency to become too thick and tangled for men and animals to pass. Many country animals do not live here because of the lack of trees and food plants. Reptiles like snakes are less common here because the climate is usually cool. However, birds, such as the Red Grouse, Merlin, Golden Plover, Meadow Pipet, Ring Ouzel, and Twite, are plentiful. Some breeds of hill sheep graze on the abundant moorland heather.

2. After Joe stumbles as he leaves, his father directs him roughly. The author tells us what was going on in Joe's mind: "He was thinking that he would never be able to understand why grownups were so hard-hearted just when you needed them most." Tell why you think Joe does not understand his father's actions.

   _____

   _____

   _____

   _____

   _____

   _____

   _____

   _____

   _____

   _____

   _____

   _____

Reading Notes

borzoi	tall slender dog with long, silky hair
iron-paling	a row of upright pointed sticks forming a fence
lea	an open space

Vocabulary: Write the meaning of each bold word or phrase.

1. She clawed **vigorously** at the wire _____

2. There was some **impulse** warning her _____

3. The heavy **foliage** swallowed her. _____

4. the **gaunt**, forbidding rock towers. _____

Comprehension Questions: Answer the following in complete sentences.

1. What does the time of day have to do with Lassie's restlessness in the pen?

_____

_____

_____

2. How is Lassie's process of escaping the pen different from how humans think?

_____

_____

_____

3. How does Joe respond differently the third time Lassie escapes the kennels?

_____

_____

_____

_____

4. How is Joe's mother tender and kind to him when he is found in the wrong?

_____

_____

_____

Quotations

1. *As Joe went upstairs he was wondering why it was that grownups sometimes were so understanding, just when you needed them most.*

2. *But his mother was patting his arm, patting it with the hand that was so clean and shiny and plump, the hand that kneaded the bread and moved so quickly when there were stockings to knit, and that danced over the needle when there was darning.*

Discussion Questions

1. What does it mean that Joe has "offended the life of the family"?
2. How had Sam known where to find Joe?
3. Why does Joe feel like the oatmeal has gotten stuck in his throat?

Enrichment

1. In this chapter, the moorlands are a place of refuge for Joe. They are high and away from the presence of others. Check out the photographs of moorlands in this book: *James Herriot's Yorkshire*, by James Herriot. New York: St. Martin's Press, 1979.

2. Lassie's intelligence and problem-solving methods will reappear in the story many times. Compare Lassie's breed (rough collie) with other kinds of collies using Wikipedia online. How are their looks and behaviors different? How are they similar?

3. Copy or write from dictation the paragraph that begins after this sentence from Sam: "Then, when I get home, I want a word with thee."

_____

_____

_____

_____

_____

_____

_____

_____

_____

_____

_____

_____

_____

Reading Notes

Yorkshire pudding	baked pancake batter with drippings of gravy
akimbo	with hands on hips and elbows bent
gesticulate	to make or use gestures
brass	money

Vocabulary: Write the meaning of each bold word or phrase.

1. obstacles which even she could not **surmount** _____

2. Joe's father **asserted** firmly. _____

3. But if a man's really got any **gumption**, he gives 'em that much. _____

_____

Comprehension Questions: Answer the following in complete sentences.

1. What kinds of "things" are not as they used to be?

_____

_____

_____

2. What difference does Lassie's absence make for Joe, and what does she symbolize?

_____

_____

_____

3. In what ways do Joe's father and mother try to protect him from grownup worries?

_____

_____

4. What is one virtue Sam puts above money and Lassie? What proves it?

_____

_____

5. Why is Sam so sure Lassie will never return?

_____

_____

Discussion Questions

1. Why do you think Sam calls walking a "champion thing to do"?

2. Throughout the story so far, Mrs. Carraclough has sometimes snapped at and talked hard at Sam, but he does not often get angry with her. What he calls "gumption" could also be thought of as considerateness and charity. What has he taken into consideration about her that gives him such a charitable attitude?

Enrichment

1. Draw a picture of Joe and Sam out on the moor just before they head back to the village. Try to convey the idea that Sam is trying to comfort and instruct his son.

2. Look at the map of the British Isles in the Appendix. Use the scale that represents distance to figure how far Yorkshire is to the Duke's estate in Scotland.

3. The following sentence is what you might call a witty saying or aphorism: "Put it in your pipe and smoke it." Write a paragraph that ends with this saying.

_____

_____

_____

_____

_____

_____

Reading Notes

cob   a short-legged, sturdy horse with a high step

hack   an old or worn-out horse

girth   band under a horse keeping the saddle in place

bedlam   a scene of wild uproar

Vocabulary: Write the meaning of each bold word or phrase.

1. the **industrial** centers of Europe. _____

2. his sturdy grey hack **ambled** along _____

3. but his entire family … had **conspired** _____

4. Pooh—this modern **generation**. _____

Comprehension Questions: Answer the following in complete sentences.

1. Name the main landmarks you would see by train going from Yorkshire to the Duke's estate.

   _____

   _____

   _____

   _____

   _____

   _____

2. Approximately how long would it take by train to travel to the Duke's estate?

   _____

   _____

3. What do the Duke's thoughts about Priscilla's riding, her going to school, and her "impertinence" reveal?

   _____

   _____

   _____

   _____

4. Despite Lassie's care and training, why is she different from the Duke's other dogs?

_____

_____

_____

5. Why does the Duke order Hynes to start walking Lassie every day?

_____

_____

_____

Quotations

Dark night falls early as you travel, for this land is in a high latitude where the sun sinks early and rises late. But your train would go on and on, screaming in the darkness as it raced over bridges, crossing rivers, crossing at last the Tweed River, which means that you are leaving England behind.

Discussion Questions

1. Why does the author tell us about traveling from Yorkshire to the Scottish Highlands?
2. A "captive" usually refers to a person who is captured and made a prisoner. Why does the author use this word to describe Lassie?

Enrichment

1. On the map of Lassie's Journey in the Appendix, see the probable train route from Yorkshire to the approximate location of the Duke's estate. Note and label any major landmarks along the route.
2. Scotland is a land of history and mystery. It was the country William Wallace and Robert the Bruce fought to defend, and it was the home of many famous writers, such as the poet Robert Burns, the mystery author Sir Arthur Conan Doyle, and the popular fantasy novelist J. K. Rowling. Traditional instruments of Scotland include the bagpipe, fiddle, and accordion. Read more about Scotland in *Scotland*, by Anita Ganeri and Chris Oxlade. Chicago: Heinmanne Library, 2003.

Reading Notes

fettle   health or condition

wrought-iron   made of iron

Vocabulary: Write the meaning of each bold word or phrase.

1. she jumped away to **elude** him. _____

2. tone which he thought might be **alluring**. _____

3. the **rendezvous** she would keep was hundreds of miles away_____

4. watching the dog go steadily at a **lope** _____

Comprehension Questions: Answer the following in complete sentences.

1. What two instincts conflict in Lassie when she becomes free from Hynes' leash?

_____

_____

_____

_____

2. Describe how Lassie escapes from Hynes.

_____

_____

_____

_____

3. How does Lassie escape the walls of the estate?

_____

_____

4. Why does Priscilla help Lassie?

_____

_____

_____

_____

_____

Discussion Questions

1. Why is Hynes especially anxious about losing Lassie?
2. What do you think the Duke means by saying, "Well, drat my buttons"?

Enrichment

1. In these past two chapters there have been references to a few interesting facts about culture, or the way people live in a certain society, in Scotland. For example, at the end of this chapter, the Duke and Priscilla are just arriving back from a trip to a local fishing village. Do you know of a fishing village near your home? In the chapter before, Priscilla and the Duke talk about her attending a school in Switzerland. Do any children you know go to a school in another country? Different peoples and countries have their own ways, sometimes similar to and sometimes different from yours. You will have noticed one dish made by the Carracloughs called Yorkshire Pudding. Try making some with your family using the recipe below:

   Ingredients:
   3/4 cup all purpose flour
   1/2 teaspoon salt
   3 eggs
   3/4 cup milk
   pan drippings from roast beef

   Directions:
   Preheat oven to 450 degrees F.
   Stir together the flour and salt in a bowl. In another bowl, beat the eggs and milk until light and foamy. Stir in the dry ingredients just until incorporated. Pour the drippings into a 9-inch pan, cast-iron skillet, or square baking dish. Put the pan in the oven and get the drippings smoking hot. Carefully take the pan out of the oven and pour in batter. Put the pan back in the oven and cook until puffed and dry, 15 to 20 minutes.

2. We have met several interesting characters in our story so far. In them we have seen wisdom, foolishness, love, dislike, fear, courage, and other virtues and vices. Pick one character and describe how he or she shows one of these qualities.

_____

_____

_____

_____

_____

_____

_____

_____

Reading Notes

homespun   plain, coarse cloth spun of yarn at home

chinnin   talking or chatting

Vocabulary: Write the meaning of each bold word or phrase.

1. there was indecision in her **gait**. _____

2. Her muscles paced with inexorable **rhythm** _____

3. She did not pause or **hesitate**. _____

4. **torrents** of rain lashed down in one of the wild storms _____

Comprehension Questions: Answer the following in complete sentences.

1. Identify and describe any new characters.

   _____

   _____

   _____

2. At the outset of Lassie's journey, how does the author contrast the ways humans and dogs travel?

   _____

   _____

   _____

   _____

   _____

3. By chasing Lassie and throwing the rock, what does the village man teach her?

   _____

   _____

4. Give examples of how Lassie uses her abilities on the first day of the journey.

   _____

   _____

   _____

5. What details of the first two days hint that it will be a long and difficult journey?

_____

_____

_____

Discussion Questions

1. Did you discover what age Lassie is?
2. What obstacles do you imagine are in store for Lassie?

Enrichment

1. On the map of Lassie's Journey in the Appendix, place a mark about 10 miles southwest of the Duke's estate and label it, "1st day: 1st lesson." Place another mark 10 miles southwest of that mark and label it, "2nd day: storm."

2. The accents in the Scottish Highlands are different from those in Yorkshire, England. For example, the sound made by the letters **ou**, as in the word **route**, are pronounced like the letters **oo**, as in boot. There are also some Scottish words and expressions that appear in this chapter. **Och**, for example, is an expression of disapproval, surprise, or regret. Find the accented words in the following sentences and write their correct spellings.

   "It looks like that fine collie belongin' tae the laird. It is! I'll sweer on it. I saw it twa days back when I were up chinnin' to McWheen aboot the salmon season. It'll be escaped, no doot …"

3. Copy or write from dictation the first paragraph of the chapter.

_____

_____

_____

_____

_____

_____

_____

_____

_____

_____

Reading Notes

terrier	small dog breed noted for courage and hunting rodents.
gorse	spiny shrub with fragrant yellow flowers and black seed pods
bracken	weedy, rough ferns with large triangular leaves or fronds

Vocabulary: Write the meaning of each bold word or phrase.

1. the low ground of **ravines** _____

2. Dropping his **quarry**, he turned to face the menace. _____

3. She did not kill **wantonly** _____

4. And the heart was **gallant** _____

Comprehension Questions: Answer the following in complete sentences.

1. What demand does Lassie begin to feel on the fifth day of her travels?

   _____

   _____

2. How does this demand cause instinct to overrule habit?

   _____

   _____

   _____

   _____

3. What is the "sensible law of nature" that Lassie acquires the fifth day?

   _____

   _____

   _____

4. Because Lassie is no longer under human care, how is she changing? What stays the same?

   _____

   _____

   _____

   _____

Quotations

1. *Lassie found the way. She did not reason it out as a human being would. Human beings have imagination—they can picture events and circumstances before they meet them. Dogs cannot do this, they must wait blindly until the circumstance faces them and they do their best to meet it.*

2. *It was instinct that drove Lassie daily in one direction. ... It was instinct that told her how to keep out of their sight—to follow the low ground of ravines, to glide belly-low on the skylines. Instinct taught her to find food.*

Discussion Questions

1. What is imagination?
2. What is instinct?

Enrichment

1. On the map of Lassie's Journey in the Appendix, place a mark a little north of Inverness and label it, "5th day: 1st meal."

2. Draw what you imagined the scene between Lassie and the weasel looked like. Remember to include as many helpful details from the story's description as you can.

3. Find the definitions of "imagination" and "instinct" in a dictionary, and write them here:

   _____

   _____

4. Imagination and instinct are different. Think of two or three ways they differ, and write a paragraph below. Remember to start with a topic sentence; use the first sentence in these directions as a model.

   _____

   _____

   _____

   _____

   _____

   _____

   _____

   _____

   _____

   _____

   _____

Reading Notes

trim   to balance a boat to sit level in the water by shifting its contents

bow   the front end of a boat

Vocabulary: Write the meaning of each bold word or phrase.

1. who **dourly** welcomed him _____

2. to a position of **vantage** _____

3. his undoubtably **prejudiced** opinion _____

4. would bring her to an **impasse** against the great lochs _____

Comprehension Questions: Answer the following in complete sentences.

1. Identify and describe any new characters.

   _____

   _____

   _____

2. What time of year is it when Mr. Freeth comes to paint at the McBanes'?

   _____

   _____

3. Why is Mr. Freeth so amazed that the dog is going to walk around the loch?

   _____

   _____

   _____

4. What characteristics do you find in Scottish people like Mr. McBane?

   _____

   _____

5. The lochs are a great and fearful barrier to Lassie's journey. Describe how they hamper her instinctual beeline south.

   _____

   _____

   _____

Quotations

"It's got business somewheer, and it's ganging aboot its business wi'oot asking help fra' no ither body on the face o' this airrth. And … it's an example which all the rest of us micht do weel to follow."

Discussion Questions

1. What does McBane mean in the quote above?
2. The author gives us two ways of seeing the lochs of Scotland: an artist's viewpoint and a wandering dog's. What is different about them?

Enrichment

1. On the map of Lassie's Journey in the Appendix, place a mark above Loch Ness and label it, "The lochs."
2. The author of this book, Eric Knight, was also an artist like Mr. Freeth. In an encyclopedia, find a photograph of one of these famous lochs of Scotland: Loch Ness, Loch Lochy, Loch Katrine, Loch Lomond, or Loch Tay. Try to draw your own version of the loch using the photograph(s) you find. You may want to add a collie in your drawing.
3. Copy or write from dictation the paragraph after this sentence: "She could not know that the instinctive straight line toward home would bring her to an impasse against the great lochs of Scotland."

_____

_____

_____

_____

_____

_____

_____

_____

_____

_____

_____

_____

_____

Reading Notes

eddie   small whirlpool

grouse   a plump, brown or gray, chicken-like game bird

Vocabulary: Write the meaning of each bold word or phrase.

1. on the right forefoot a thorn was **festering** _____

2. But it was a **tumultuous**, fast-charging river_____

3. They had now almost stiffened to **immobility**. _____

4. A **ravening** hunger woke in her_____

Comprehension Questions: Answer the following in complete sentences.

1. Once Lassie's walk around the loch is ending, what has the loch become?

_____

_____

2. Besides the festering thorn, what other injury does Lassie have once she comes out of the river?

_____

_____

3. Describe what happens during the nine days Lassie recuperates in the gorse thicket.

_____

_____

_____

_____

_____

_____

4. After her recuperation in the thicket, how is Lassie different from when she left the Duke's estate? How is she the same?

_____

_____

_____

_____

Quotations

The greatness, or the smallness, of a distance do not qualify in the minds of an animal. All she knew was that she felt satisfied. She had made her way in the direction in which she wanted to go more than she wanted anything else in life. She breathed happily.

Discussion Questions

1. The author, Eric Knight, was a graduate of the Cambridge School of Latin in Massachusetts. Like many people in his time period, he had heard and read about the stories of ancient Greece and Rome. Is there anything in this chapter that reflects his knowledge of classical literature?
2. Even though Lassie is an animal, she can be an example to humans. What admirable qualities does she model for us in this chapter?

Enrichment

1. On the map of Lassie's Journey in the Appendix, place a mark near the southwest tip of Loch Ness and label it, "gorse thicket."
2. We have come across several fauna, or wildlife, during Lassie's journey in Scotland. Make a list of the animals she has encountered so far, and then look up "Fauna of Scotland" on Wikipedia. Discover what other animals might be found along Lassie's route.
3. Find a picture of heather and observe its characteristics. Color the picture of heather flowers in the Appendix.
4. The author tells Lassie's story well because he has observed animals closely. Having owned a collie like Lassie, he learned about their behavior, instincts, and qualities, such as their ability to sense danger with sharp hearing and smell. Think of an animal or pet you have known or observed. Tell something you know about the way it behaves in a paragraph below.

_____

_____

_____

_____

_____

_____

_____

_____

_____

_____

Reading Notes

croft	a small enclosed field next to a house
tweed	a coarse wool cloth with many weaves and colors
tam-o-shanter	a round, flat-topped cap with a pompom at its center
cur	an inferior dog

Vocabulary: Write the meaning of each bold word or phrase.

1. the long **vigil** was at last over. _____

2. They're that **canny**, lad, it passes understanding. _____

3. the **tedium** was too much for him. _____

4. It was **armistice**. _____

Comprehension Questions: Answer the following in complete sentences.

1. Identify and describe any new characters.

   _____

   _____

2. Why are Jock and Andrew waiting in the croft?

   _____

   _____

   _____

   _____

3. Why do Jock and Andrew say dogs are their greatest helper and greatest enemy?

   _____

   _____

   _____

4. How long has it been since Lassie has left the gorse thicket?

   _____

   _____

5. How does Lassie's way of fighting Jock and Andrew's dogs show pure breeding?

_____

_____

_____

6. Why does Jock decide not to shoot Lassie once the other dogs give up fighting?

_____

_____

_____

Discussion Questions

1. What more do we learn about Scottish people from this chapter?

2. What more do we learn about Lassie?

Enrichment

1. On the map of Lassie's Journey in the Appendix, place a mark midway between the "Highlands" and "Lowlands" and label it, "The croft."

2. Look up the "Black Watch" in an encyclopedia and read about the historical account of its part in World War I.

3. Go to a fabric store and buy some "Black Watch Plaid." Use it to make a handkerchief, pillowcase, or something more elaborate.

4. Go to the Appendix and read the poem "Sir Galahad," by Alfred, Lord Tennyson. How does Andrew make use of the story of Galahad? How is Lassie like this mythical knight of the Round Table?

5. Copy or write from dictation the paragraph that begins after this sentence: "He lay in a moment of surrender."

_____

_____

_____

_____

_____

_____

_____

_____

_____

_____

Reading Notes

tattoo	a continuous drumming or beating, like heavy machines
constable	police officer
waif	abandoned young child or animal

Vocabulary: Write the meaning of each bold word or phrase.

1. the only **eminences** were the "bings" _____

2. Lassie might try to **circumvent** them _____

3. she faded away … like **quicksilver**_____

4. It was aye so muddy and **forlorn** and terrible-looking _____

Comprehension Questions: Answer the following in complete sentences.

1. Identify and describe any new characters.

   _____

2. After leaving the croft, how is the landscape changing for Lassie?

   _____

3. What is Lassie's attitude toward the cities and people in the Lowlands?

   _____

   _____

4. Describe how the two Lowland women's encounters with Lassie are different.

   _____

   _____

   _____

5. What is Lassie not prepared for as she crosses the bridge? Why?

   _____

   _____

   _____

6. How is Lassie treated by the dogcatchers, and how is she defended?

   _____

   _____

Discussion Questions

1. What is unjust about some of the Lowland people's behavior towards Lassie?
2. When Ethelda remarks that the dog reminds her of her childhood dog, Bonnie, Michael says, "Well, but she was a magnificent creature, Ethelda." Why is his statement ironic?
3. Ethelda is a heroine in this chapter. What are some of her virtues, and how does she show them?

Enrichment

1. On the map of Lassie's Journey in the Appendix, place a mark near Edinburgh and label it, "Captured."
2. The dogcatchers and some others in this chapter seem to treat animals with less than kindness. It would have done them good to read the "Shaker Poem." Find it in the Appendix now and see how the Shakers thought animals should be treated.
3. People are often fooled by appearances. The appearance of someone or something does not always correspond to its value, worth, or goodness. As the saying goes, "You can't judge a book by its cover." Think of something that provides an example of this truth. Write a paragraph about this example, and use the first sentence of these directions as your topic sentence.

_____

_____

_____

_____

_____

_____

_____

_____

_____

_____

_____

_____

_____

_____

_____

_____

_____

_____

Reading Notes

mandarins	Chinese officials
Oyez	"Hear ye"; cried at the start and end of court
escutcheon	shield or a coat of arms; one's reputation

Vocabulary: Write the meaning of each bold word or phrase.

1. a **tawny** figure streaked by him _____

2. answer yes or no without **equivocation** _____

3. Then a **sombre** voice spoke. _____

4. "It is a dog!" the judge said **affably** _____

Comprehension Questions: Answer the following in complete sentences.

1. Identify and describe any new characters.

   _____

   _____

   _____

2. What about Lassie's actions mislead and lull Fergusson as he gets her out of the van and walks down the corridor?

   _____

   _____

   _____

3. Lassie's entrance into the court, the judge's witty comments, the consternation of the Sergeant, and the clamor of the young men add what to this scene in the story?

   _____

   _____

4. Why is Lassie's final escape from the dogcatchers so amazing?

   _____

   _____

   _____

5. What ruins the dogcatchers' plan to leave Lassie's escape unreported?

_____

_____

6. What is the irony in Fergusson's conclusion and moral to Donnell?

_____

_____

_____

_____

_____

Discussion Questions

1. Stories have something called a "narrative flow" that refers to how each part of the story relates to those right before and after it. The end of a chapter, for example, can often hint at what might happen in the next one. What are some connections between this chapter and the one before that create a narrative flow?

Enrichment

1. Draw and color what you imagine the scene in the courtroom looked like.

2. The loyalty of Lassie to the Carracloughs and her home in Yorkshire shows up again and again as we see her persevere in her journey. There is another story of this kind of loyalty that comes from the city of Edinburgh in the Lowlands. It is the factual story of a dog named Bobby, known by those in Edinburgh as Greybriars Bobby. Read about Bobby in the Appendix. Your parents might also like this story, which has been made into a book and movie. You can learn more about Greyfriars Bobby online.

3. To write a story set partly in Scotland, the author had to be accurate with his depictions of Scottish people and places. For example, the names of people should be of Scottish or English origin. Check to see if that is the case in this story by looking up some of the names you came across in this chapter (e.g., McQuarrie, Fergusson). Use a book about names or look them up on Wikipedia.

4. Copy or write from dictation the paragraph that follows this sentence: "In that flash, Lassie was free."

_____

_____

_____

_____

_____

_____

_____

_____

Reading Notes

thrush	a dull brown and speckled medium-sized songbird
scuttle	a metal pan for carrying coal
shilling	a coin used in the United Kingdom, worth 1/20 of a pound each
purl	a stitch in knitting

Vocabulary: Write the meaning of each bold word or phrase.

1. the small **pension** that the Government paid _____

2. the light glowed **incandescent** _____

3. The woman caught his **ominous** tone. _____

4. the woman repeated **stolidly**. _____

Comprehension Questions: Answer the following in complete sentences.

1. Identify and describe any new characters.

   _____

   _____

2. Describe Lassie's swim over the Tweed River.

   _____

   _____

3. What is significant about the Tweed River?

   _____

   _____

4. What kind of people are the Faddens, and what loss do they bear?

   _____

   _____

5. What do the Faddens do for Lassie?

   _____

6. Why is Dally worried about Lassie's owner coming for her?

   _____

   _____

Quotations

Ah, war—machine wars. Bullets took them all. The brave and the cowardly, the weak and the fine strong ones like Dannie. And it wasn't the dying that took bravery, then, for cowards could die. It was the living that took bravery—living in that mud and rain and cold and keeping the spirit strong through it all. That was the bravery. And how often she pictured it, when the winds blew and the cold rain slatted.

Discussion Questions

1. Why do you think Dan never follows through with killing the goose for Christmas?
2. Why do the cold, wet nights remind Dally of Dannie?
3. Compare and contrast Lassie's trials with Dannie's.
4. What has Lassie become for Dally?

Enrichment

1. On the map of Lassie's Journey in the Appendix, place a mark on the Tweed River where it acts as the border of Scotland and England and label it, "Crosses the border." Place another mark slightly to the south and label it, "The Faddens."
2. The northeast wind, called the "easters" by Dan, are so fierce that they have a poem written about them. Read "Ode to the Northeast Wind" in the Appendix.
3. Read the section on theme in "Literary Tools" in the Appendix.
4. Stories in literature are written with specific themes, or repeated ideas, that show up in characters and events. Some major themes in our story include poverty, courage, and the kindness of strangers. Pick one of these themes and give examples where it appears in a character or event in the story. Your topic sentence should start, "One theme in this story is …."

_____

_____

_____

_____

_____

_____

_____

_____

_____

_____

_____

_____

Reading Notes

flagging   a pavement laid with flat stone slabs, or flagstones

bonnie   pleasing, agreeable, good

Vocabulary: Write the meaning of each bold word or phrase.

1. as they had **christened** Lassie. _____

2. to be **harried** on its way with a flung stone. _____

3. and try again to **wean** its mind from old memories. _____

4. and patted her **consolingly**. _____

Comprehension Questions: Answer the following in complete sentences.

1. As Lassie recovers at the Faddens', what awakens in her?

 _____

 _____

 _____

2. How can the Faddens tell that Lassie is not happy in their cottage anymore?

 _____

 _____

 _____

3. What does Dally say Lassie's stay with them is like?

 _____

 _____

 _____

4. Describe the three types of people that relate to dogs. What type are the Faddens?

 _____

 _____

 _____

5. What proves the Faddens' noble and kind nature towards Lassie?

 _____

 _____

Discussion Questions

1. How are the Faddens like the Carracloughs?
2. What is the significance of this chapter's title?
3. What virtues do you see in Dally and Dan?
4. How long does Lassie stay with the Faddens, and about how long has she been on her journey altogether?

Enrichment

1. Draw a sketch of what you imagine the Faddens' cottage looks like on the inside. Remember to include Dally's rocking chair, the hearth and coal skuttle, the door and window where Lassie paces, and the floor of flagging.

2. Copy or write from dictation the paragraph that begins after this sentence: "She was going south again."

_____

_____

_____

_____

_____

_____

_____

_____

_____

Reading Notes

cudgel	a short, thick stick
mountebank	a salesman who attracts customers by deceiving them
phaeton	a light four-wheeled open carriage
brazier	a simple charcoal grill

Vocabulary: Write the meaning of each bold word or phrase.

1. He began singing **lustily** _____

2. his doleful story of the **hapless** village maiden. _____

3. a great, broad, rich **swathe** _____

4. as the housewives fingered his **wares** _____

Comprehension Questions: Answer the following in complete sentences.

1. Describe Rowlie's business, his company, and his character.

   _____

   _____

   _____

   _____

   _____

2. Why does Lassie turn down the pieces of liver Rowlie drops?

   _____

   _____

3. Describe how Rowlie gets Lassie to trust him.

   _____

   _____

4. Why does Rowlie change the direction of his travel?

   _____

   _____

   _____

5. How do Lassie and Toots act differently? Why?

_____

_____

_____

_____

Quotations

His mind was not on the words. Instead, as always, his senses were alert to the world about him. Travelling and living in the open as he did, Rowlie knew a good deal about his world. He knew where magpies nested and when the swallows came and went. And no huntsman in the land had an eye any quicker than Rowlie's for seeing the whisp of red that was a fox.

Discussion Questions

1. Lassie has had several names given to her in the story. What are some examples?
2. Why does Rowlie call Lassie "Her Majesty"?

Enrichment

1. On the map of Lassie's Journey in the Appendix, place a mark halfway between the Faddens and Durham and label it "Meets Rowlie."
2. Eric Knight, the author, had a dog named "Toots." Read about Eric and Toots in the Biographical Sketch in the Appendix.
3. Rowlie is a good example of a man who has his eyes open to the world around him. He is wise, as we see by his interaction with others, because he has a mind that is "awake." By knowing the world around you, you are better able to make wise decisions in it. Think about your world. What are the main places in your world? Who are the main people? What are the main things going on around you? Answer these questions in a paragraph below.

_____

_____

_____

_____

_____

_____

_____

_____

_____

_____

Reading Notes

grouse	to grumble or complain
hawker	one who sells wares by calling out in the street
footpads	robbers or highwaymen who travel on foot

Vocabulary: Write the meaning of each bold word or phrase.

1. The big man halted his **tirade** _____

2. He stepped out boldly, now that **concealment** was gone _____

3. Now all **pretence** was gone. _____

4. a **tarpaulin** buttoned over his knees _____

Comprehension Questions: Answer the following in complete sentences.

1. Identify and describe any new characters.

   _____

   _____

2. What do Buckles and Snickers try to do to Rowlie?

   _____

3. How is Toots killed?

   _____

4. What makes Lassie run away at first? What "older force" in Lassie wins?

   _____

   _____

5. Why does Rowlie let Lassie go?

   _____

   _____

   _____

6. As Rowlie arrives home, what is Lassie facing?

   _____

   _____

Quotations

"There are six things the Lord hates, yes, seven of which are an abomination to Him: haughty eyes, a lying tongue, and hands that shed innocent blood, a heart that devises wicked plans, feet that run quickly to evil, a false witness who speaks lies, and one who spreads strife among friends." Proverbs 6:16-19

Discussion Questions

1. While Rowlie, the Faddens, Ethelda, and other characters have shown virtues, Buckles and Snickers show vices. Seven vices are described in the quotation above. Which ones do Buckles and Snickers show, and how?

Enrichment

1. On the map of Lassie's Journey in the Appendix, place a mark near the border of Yorkshire and label it, "Leaves Rowlie."
2. Tea is a popular treat throughout the British Isles. You may have learned from reading *Lassie Come-Home*, however, that "tea" does not just mean a hot beverage brewed from tea leaves. Read about the culture of Tea Time in the Appendix. Brew some tea using the instructions, and have a cup yourself with a sweet morsel, such as a scone or cookie.
3. Copy or write from dictation the paragraph that begins after this sentence: "He advanced, smiled."

_____

_____

_____

_____

_____

_____

_____

_____

_____

_____

_____

_____

_____

_____

_____

_____

Reading Notes

tor and brae	rocky peaks and hillsides
beck and burn	brooks and streams
blue-merly	color with irregular spots of pattern
touched	slightly crazy
filly	young female horse

Vocabulary: Write the meaning of each bold word or phrase.

1. and let his hands travel over the **emaciated** frame_____

2. smack up against **elemental** truths. _____

3. I **presume**, of course_____

4. Sam Carraclough stooped, **perplexed**._____

Comprehension Questions: Answer the following in complete sentences.

1. How far from Yorkshire is the Duke's estate in Scotland for a man? and for a dog?

    _____

    _____

2. Describe what the Carracloughs do in order to save Lassie and nurse her to health.

    _____

    _____

3. What reason does Joe give his mother for convincing his father to lie to the Duke?

    _____

    _____

4. What does Sam do to Lassie? Why is the Duke not truly fooled by this?

    _____

    _____

    _____

5. Why is it ironic that the Carracoughs assume the Duke has come to get Lassie?

    _____

    _____

Quotations

1. *Lying, cheating, stealing — they were wrong, and you couldn't make them right by twisting them round in your mind. ... But a man has to live with his family, too. When a woman starts to argue with a man ... well ...*

2. *But the Duke of Rudling knew many things too — many, many things. ... Slowly, as if he were in a dream, he knelt down, and his hand made one gentle movement. It picked up a forepaw and turned it slightly. So he knelt by the collie, looking with eyes that were as knowing about dogs as any man in Yorkshire.*

Discussion Questions

1. What are the two virtues or absolutes with which Sam struggles as he decides what to do?
2. What would you have done in Sam's place?
3. Why is it ironic that Sam copes Lassie?
4. Who proves to be a wise and understanding person in this chapter, and why?

Enrichment

1. On the map of Lassie's Journey in the Appendix, place a mark in Yorkshire and label it, "Home."
2. This story has been filled with interesting, lively characters. Who, besides Lassie, is your favorite character? Describe how you see this character in a paragraph below. Begin with, "My favorite character is …."

_____

_____

_____

_____

_____

_____

_____

_____

_____

_____

_____

_____

_____

_____

Reading Notes

hollyhooks	tall plants grown for their showy, colorful flower clusters
sculler	small room next to kitchen where food is cleaned, trimmed
tureen	broad, deep covered dish for serving soup of stew
blarney	to flatter someone

Vocabulary: Write the meaning of each bold word or phrase.

1. a strong **constitution** aided her now. _____

2. Joe **disclaimed** _____

3. He still **crooned** to the dog. _____

4. she's got a **litter** _____

Comprehension Questions: Answer the following in complete sentences.

1. How does Lassie come to look almost as perfect as she had once been?

   _____

   _____

   _____

2. Why is Joe's promise to the Duke that Lassie will always be waiting for him wrong?

   _____

   _____

3. Since Lassie has returned, how are things renewed in Joe's home and family?

   _____

   _____

   _____

4. According to Joe, what has caused everything to be just like old times again?

   _____

   _____

5. Describe the "secret kinship" between Joe and his father.

   _____

   _____

6. What is significant about the new name Joe gives to Lassie?

_____

_____

_____

Quotations

1. *"Ye mustn't mind women too much, Joe. They have a hard time of it, staying home and scrubbing and scouring and cooking all day, and so they take it out in scolding, and we've got to let them do it to blow off steam. But we know it doesn't really mean anything, we men know that—we men!"*

2. *"The two of ye. Ah, ye're both chips off the same stick. Ye're both saying that to blarney me."*

Discussion Questions

1. Why do you think the author has Priscilla appear in this last chapter?

2. In this chapter and the quotes above, we are reminded of Joe and Sam's relationship, which has been a subject in other chapters too. What are some ways the author has shown us that, as Mrs. Carraclough says, they are both "chips off the same stick"?

3. Lassie's new name, "Lassie Come-Home," and the dictation passage below (Enrichment #3) tell us what Lassie is and why things are right again. Based on these clues, what do you think is the main theme of the story?

Enrichment

1. In the Appendix, find the section entitled "Literary Tools." Read about the different tools authors use when they write a story, and try to identify ways Eric Knight used some of them in *Lassie Come-Home*.

2. Look up the etymology (or history) of the word "blarney" in a dictionary.

3. Copy or write from dictation the paragraph that begins after this sentence: "After the meal was over, and Lassie came stalking in, he sank on the rug beside her and stroked her, and he thought he had found the answer."

_____

_____

_____

_____

_____

_____

_____

APPENDIX

Biographical Sketch: Eric Knight

Eric Knight was born on April 10, 1897, in the village of Menston, in West Yorkshire, England. He grew up as the third of four sons in this little village, in which farms, sheep pastures, and cottages dotted the land. His father, a diamond merchant, deserted the family for South Africa when Knight was two years old, and he was later killed during the Boer War. Later, Knight's mother remarried and moved to the United States. When Eric was fifteen, Knight joined her in Cambridge, Massachusetts, where he went to school at the Cambridge School of Latin. He then became an art student at the New York National Academy School of Fine Arts.

Throughout his life Knight had several jobs. He was a teacher at the University of Iowa, a journalist, a film critic and film writer, a novelist, and a soldier in both World Wars. While he was respected in all these fields, he is most famous as a writer. He wrote several books, such as *The Happy Land*, *Invitation to Life*, *The Flying Yorkshireman*, and *This Above All*, which was a bestseller in its day. During World War II, Knight was aboard a plane over the South American country of Suriname. For causes unknown, the plane crashed in the jungle, and Knight was killed. He was 45 years old.

Although Eric Knight lived a comparatively short life, he will long be remembered for his creative work, especially for the story and character of Lassie.

When Knight married his wife, Jere, they settled on a farm in Pennsylvania, where they had many dogs. One small terrier dog was taken with them when they moved to California, but shortly after, it was hit and killed by a car. Knight then bought a female collie puppy for Jere as a Christmas present, but it soon became apparent that this dog, named Toots, had only one master: Eric! Being trained to respond to hand signals, Toots was well known for her tricks and performances while traveling with Knight on book tours across the country. He was amazed at her intelligence and eagerness to learn, but he also admired her devotion, for she would sit patiently every day in front of their house waiting for him to come home.

Along with his relationship with Toots, another special part of Knight's life was his homeland. On a trip to England during the Great Depression, he saw the character and endurance of poor English families, many of whom were forced to sell cherished possessions, even their beloved dogs. Through these experiences, the story of a loyal dog and a Yorkshire family in hard times formed in Knight's imagination. On December 17, 1938, a short story version of *Lassie Come-Home* was printed in the Saturday Evening Post. Two years later it became a best-selling book. In the fifty years since, it has been translated into twenty-five languages and inspired eight movies, a radio show, a long-running television show, and great affection among many people for this dog, Lassie.

The Industrial Revolution

The Industrial Revolution started in the late 1700s and early 1800s. It did not occur in a moment, like a spark in a fire, but continued to change the world for many years. Before the Revolution, industry, or the production of goods, was done by manual labor and work animals. Farming was the most important kind of industry. After the Industrial Revolution, however, most goods were produced by machines. Textiles (e.g., thread, cloth, fabric) had once been hand-woven and sown, but now machines like the "spinning jenny" allowed one weaver to do the work of eight. Eventually, inventors made textile machines so big that they were put into factories, where production could be multiplied by the hundreds. Mining was also greatly changed. Mines had been around before the Revolution, but at that time coal was limited to heating homes. After the Revolution, coal was needed to power steam engines, which were not only used for locomotives, but all kinds of industrial machines, such as water pumps and steamboats.

Coal mining was a big industry, but it was not easy. Miners worked in shafts dug into the earth near coal deposits. Injuries by falling rock were common, and explosions due to firedamp (flammable gas) occurred occasionally. Labor was long and difficult, with workers using pick axes and heavy iron carts. When the Great Depression hit the world in the 1930s, coal miners in northern England counties like Yorkshire were put out of work.

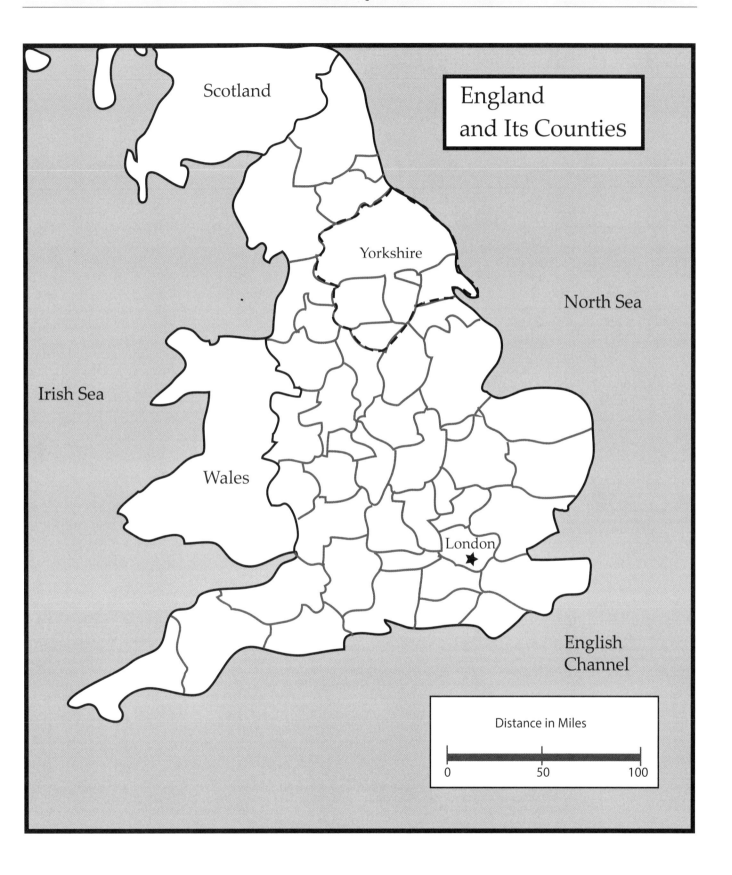

England
and Its Counties

Scotland

Yorkshire

North Sea

Irish Sea

Wales

London

English
Channel

Distance in Miles

0   50   100

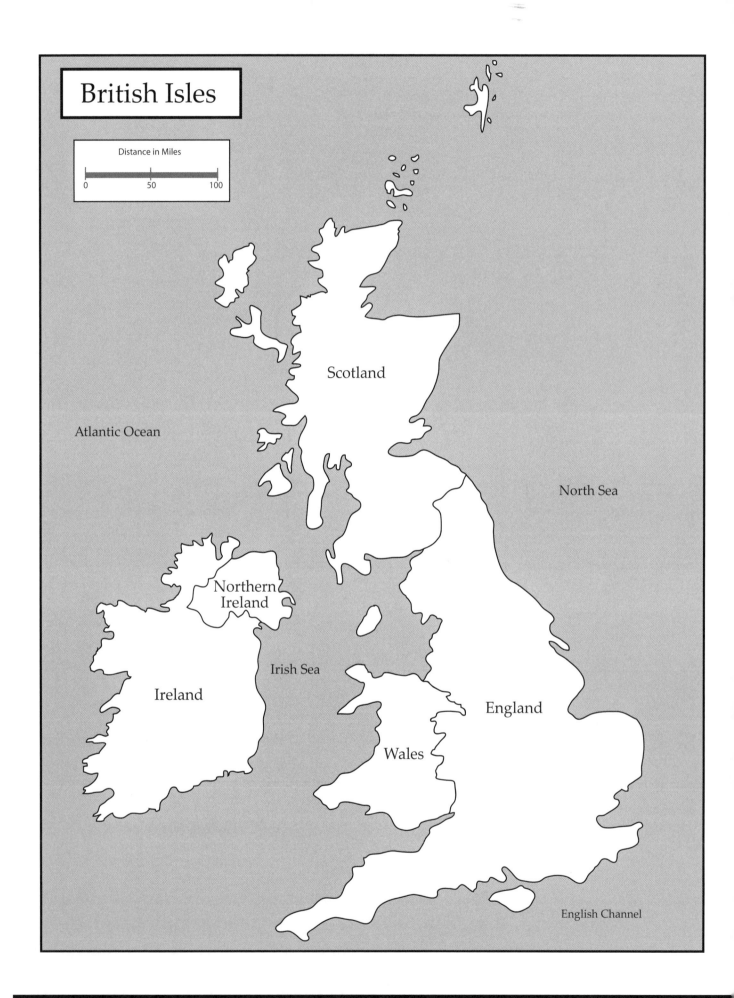

British Isles

Distance in Miles

0   50   100

Scotland

Atlantic Ocean

North Sea

Northern
Ireland

Ireland

Irish Sea

England

Wales

English Channel

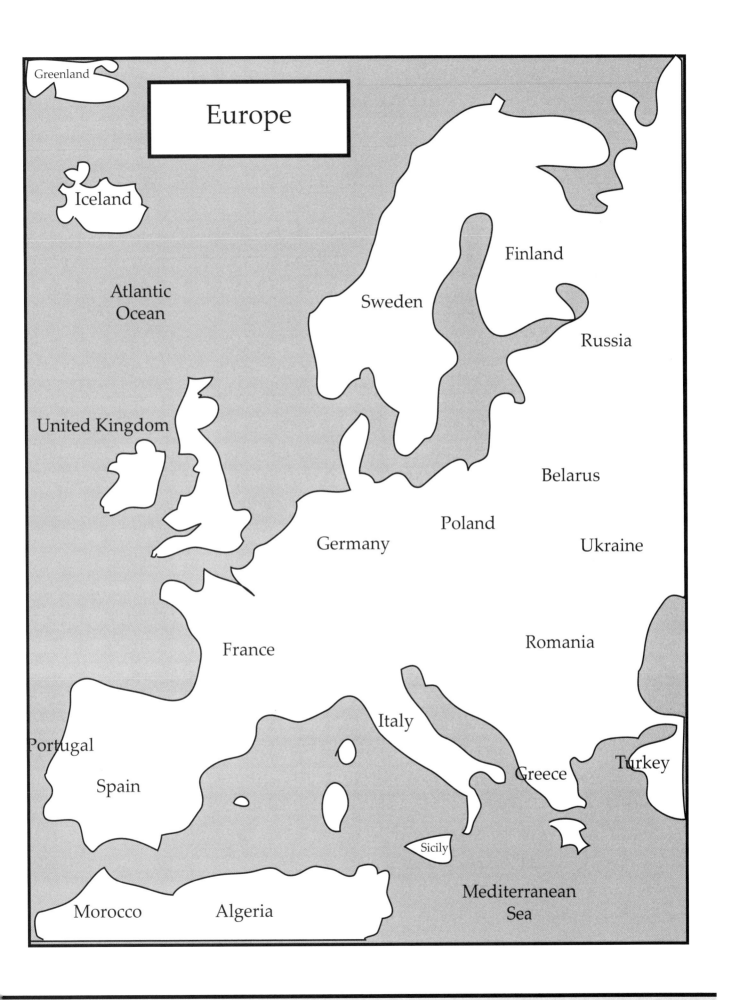

Europe

Greenland

Iceland

Atlantic
Ocean

Finland

Sweden

Russia

United Kingdom

Belarus

Poland

Ukraine

Germany

Romania

France

Italy

Portugal

Turkey

Spain

Greece

Sicily

Mediterranean
Sea

Morocco

Algeria

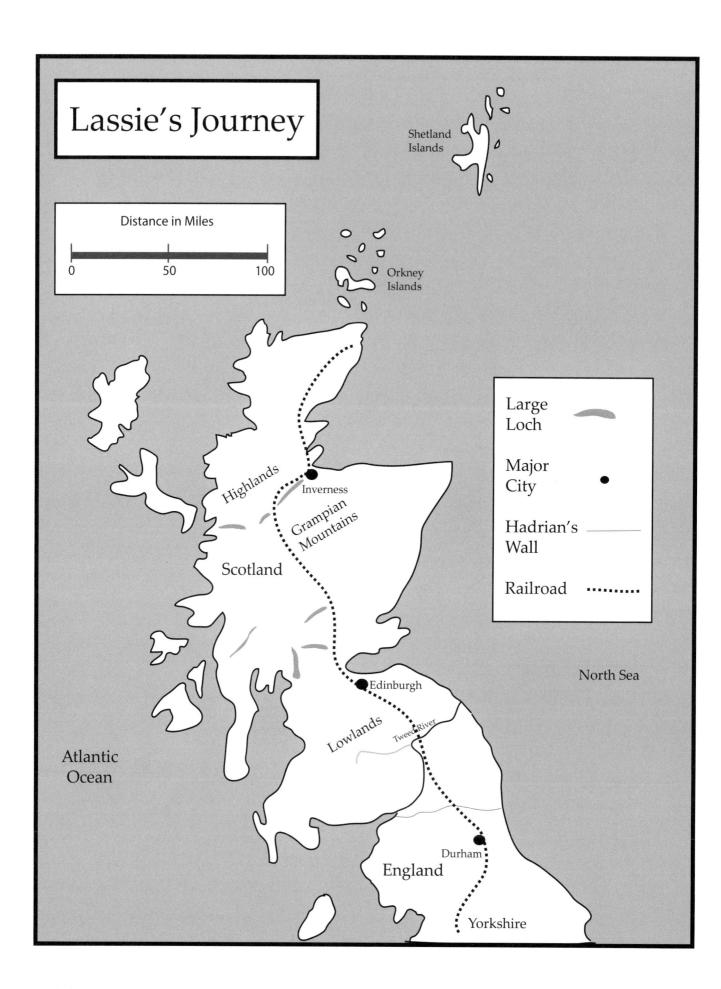

Lassie's Journey

Distance in Miles

0   50   100

Shetland Islands

Orkney Islands

Large Loch

Major City

Hadrian's Wall

Railroad

Highlands

Inverness

Grampian Mountains

Scotland

Lowlands

Edinburgh

Tweed River

North Sea

Atlantic Ocean

Durham

England

Yorkshire

PLOT is the author's arrangement of events in a story. The plot of a story is like a trail through a forest; it connects all the places, people, and happenings. There is a starting point and there is an end. Along the way you see many different things. You meet a variety of animals, like birds, squirrels, foxes, and maybe bears. The trail offers you views of dense black woods, grassy open glades, rushing streams, deep gorges and vast canyons, and, when the trail ends, a rich blue sky. Yet, while the hike is continually offering new views (characters, twists, and turns), all of it is connected somehow. The things you saw at first, the sights you see now, and the experiences that lie ahead are all joined together by what brings you to them: the trail. And that is what plot does for a story. It gives every scene a place in an overall picture, like little pieces of a puzzle that fit into a whole. Plot is, however, more than just the connection among pieces of a puzzle. Let's go a bit further by thinking about how plots and trails come to be. A trail does not appear from nowhere, and neither does a plot. Every trail is made by a trailblazer, a person who walked through the woods long before you came and cleared the path for others like you to follow. He decided where the trail would go, where it would curve, where it would descend, what obstacles it would bypass, what sights it would offer, and to what destination it would take you. In the same way, the plot of a story is also designed by its author to go on a certain course in a certain order. The author decided the path readers would take when they read his story. He decided what characters they would meet and when; he planned all the events, the ups and the downs, the funny parts and the sad ones; he created all the problems, dangers, and obstacles characters would face and how they would overcome them. All this makes a big difference to a reader's experience. Imagine if the order of a story were backwards. The reader would know the end before he knew who any of the characters were or what the book was about! A Sherlock Holmes mystery would quickly be spoiled by starting off with the end. Part of the fun of reading is walking the trail of the story, and, in Holmes' case, discovering with him the clues and solutions to the mystery as we turn the pages. Although not all stories need to follow the same kind of path, without a good arrangement of all the story's parts, readers can be confused, bored, or disappointed. And so, plot is a very important tool in literature, for it is the thing that connects and orders all the parts of a story.

CHARACTERIZATION is the author's way of creating people (or things) with human qualities in a story. Characters are usually people, but they can also be animals and even non-living objects. What makes someone or something a character is that it has human qualities, to which, in some degree, readers can relate. The first thing we usually observe about a character is outward appearance. For example, in J. R. R. Tolkien's *The Hobbit*, one of the first things we learn about Bilbo Baggins is that he is about three feet tall, middle-aged, dresses in bright-colored clothes, and has woolly (but neatly brushed) toes. These sorts of things give us an image in our head and introduce us to a character, just as if we are meeting someone for the first time and have never laid eyes on them before. The look of a character can tell us a lot of information, and yet, characterization goes beyond looks. For instance, by the look of Bilbo, no one could guess that he would be a person of great courage and boldness because, by all appearances, he is just an ordinary person who likes comfort and safety and, like all plain quiet folk, has no use for adventure. But through the course of the story, or plot, characters unfold hidden qualities that can surprise, disgust, inspire, and delight readers. Like a log in a fire, a character's traits are revealed slowly as the heat and drama of the story require them to act and show what is inside them. Readers will likely identify with the characters because of the traits and qualities that are revealed, and often readers will come away from a story feeling as if they know a character as well as they know an actual person. One may feel as if they are present in the story, too, or feel like they are one of the characters in it. And this fact points to why characters are essential to a story: a story must involve characters, since they are the ones doing the action, receiving the action, or being affected by the action. Like a sentence must have a subject to go with the predicate, a story must have characters to go along with the plot. Or, going back to our trail analogy, like a trail must have a hiker to walk it, a story's plot must have characters to experience it.

SETTING is the world created by the author in a story. The plot has to happen somewhere, and characters can't exist without an environment around them. A trail is only a trail if it has a wilderness around it, and a plot is only a plot if it has a setting in which to unfold. The author creates a setting for a story by revealing and describing things like place (e.g., Kansas, the land of Oz), time (e.g., 1940s, "In the Beginning"), and the kind of society in which characters live (e.g., Medieval Europe, Nazi Germany). For example, George Lucas gives his story a setting of time and place right away with these opening words: "A long time ago, in a galaxy far, far away …." Although this is a short description of setting, it tells us enough to know that the world we are about to enter is not on planet Earth nor in any part of Earth's recorded history. The way an author describes the world of a story has a big effect on the way we experience it. Most often, setting provides a mood or feeling for readers to sense and connect with the actions and development of characters. The following passage helps give the setting for Chapter 2 of Charles Dickens' *A Tale of Two Cities* by describing the road on which a night coach is driving; but it does more than tell us where the coach is:

> There was a steaming mist in all the hollows, and it had roamed in its forlornness up the hill, like an evil spirit, seeking rest and finding none. A clammy and intensely cold mist, it made its slow way through the air in ripples that visibly followed and overspread one another, as the waves of an unwholesome sea might do. It was dense enough to shut out everything from the light of the coach-lamps but these its own workings, and a few yards of road; and the reek of the laboring horses steamed into it, as if they had made it all.

What is the mood given off by this description of setting? Is it bright, happy, and carefree? Or does it give a reader the sense that something mysterious or ominous is afoot? Setting not only places characters and plot into a world, it places the reader there too.

THEME has to do with the meaning an author intends for a story. While some stories may only have one intended meaning or theme (e.g., Nathan's story to David about the ewe lamb is mainly meant to show David his guilt), most stories have many themes that show the points an author wishes to make. It's also important to know that themes are not just ideas, but what an author says about the ideas. For example, in *Lassie Come-Home*, a major theme has to with Lassie's undying devotion to the Carracloughs; the theme is not simply undying devotion, but that undying devotion like Lassie's is praiseworthy and should be a model for people to imitate. Themes are not usually easy to find, and one must read a story carefully to really understand what the author intends it to mean. Here are some hints to help you read with a better eye for theme:

- Pay attention to the title of a story and ask how it relates to the story itself.
- Ask, "What do the characters learn through their experiences?"
- Watch for things that seem to appear again and again, or details that might symbolize something deeper than themselves (e.g., the One Ring in *The Lord of the Rings*).

"Sir Galahad" by Alfred, Lord Tennyson

My good blade carves the casques of men,
  My tough lance thrusteth sure,
My strength is as the strength of ten,
  Because my heart is pure.
The shattering trumpet shrilleth high,
  The hard brands shiver on the steel,
The splinter'd spear-shafts crack and fly,
  The horse and rider reel:
They reel, they roll in clanging lists,
  And when the tide of combat stands,
Perfume and flowers fall in showers,
  That lightly rain from ladies' hands.

How sweet are looks that ladies bend
  On whom their favours fall!
From them I battle till the end,
  To save from shame and thrall:
But all my heart is drawn above,
  My knees are bow'd in crypt and shrine:
I never felt the kiss of love,
  Nor maiden's hand in mine.
More bounteous aspects on me beam,
  Me mightier transports move and thrill;
So keep I fair thro' faith and prayer
  A virgin heart in work and will.

When down the stormy crescent goes,
  A light before me swims,
Between dark stems the forest glows,
  I hear a noise of hymns:
Then by some secret shrine I ride;
  I hear a voice but none are there;
The stalls are void, the doors are wide,
  The tapers burning fair.
Fair gleams the snowy altar-cloth,
  The silver vessels sparkle clean,
The shrill bell rings, the censer swings,
  And solemn chaunts resound between.

Sometime on lonely mountain-meres
  I find a magic bark;
I leap on board: no helmsman steers:
  I float till all is dark.
A gentle sound, an awful light!
  Three angels bear the holy Grail:
With folded feet, in stoles of white,
  On sleeping wings they sail.
Ah, blessed vision! blood of God!
  My spirit beats her mortal bars,
As down dark tides the glory slides,
  And star-like mingles with the stars.

When on my goodly charger borne
  Thro' dreaming towns I go,
The cock crows ere the Christmas morn,
  The streets are dumb with snow.
The tempest crackles on the leads,
  And, ringing, springs from brand and mail;
But o'er the dark a glory spreads,
  And gilds the driving hail.
I leave the plain, I climb the height;
  No branchy thicket shelter yields;
But blessed forms in whistling storms
  Fly o'er waste fens and windy fields.

A maiden knight—to me is given
  Such hope, I know not fear;
I yearn to breathe the airs of heaven
  That often meet me here.
I muse on joy that will not cease,
  Pure spaces clothed in living beams,
Pure lilies of eternal peace,
  Whose odours haunt my dreams;
And, stricken by an angel's hand,
  This mortal armour that I wear,
This weight and size, this heart and eyes,
  Are touch'd, are turn'd to finest air.

The clouds are broken in the sky,
  And thro' the mountain-walls
A rolling organ-harmony
  Swells up, and shakes and falls.
Then move the trees, the copses nod,
  Wings flutter, voices hover clear:
"O just and faithful knight of God!
  Ride on! the prize is near."
So pass I hostel, hall, and grange;
  By bridge and ford, by park and pale,
All-arm'd I ride, whate'er betide
  Until I find the holy Grail

–Alfred, Lord Tennyson

A man of kindness to his beast is kind;

brutal actions show a brutal mind.

Remember He who made the brute,

who gave thee speech and reason,

formed him mute.

He can't complain but God's omniscient eye,

beholds thy cruelty,

He hears his cry.

He was destined thy servant and thy drudge,

But know this: His creator is thy judge.

Ode to the Northeast Wind

Welcome, wild Northeaster!
Shame it is to see
Odes to every zephyr;
Ne'er a verse to thee.
Welcome black Northeaster!
O'er the German foam;
O'ver the Danish moorlands,
From thy frozen home.
Tired are we of summer,
Tired of gaudy glare,
Showers soft and steaming,
Hot and breathless air.
Tired of listless dreaming,
Through the lazy day—
Jovial wind of winter
Turn us out to play!
Sweep the golden reed-beds;
Crisp the lazy dike;
Hunger into madness
Every plunging pike.
Fill the lake with wild fowl;
Fill the marsh with snipe;
While on dreary moorlands
Lonely curlew pipe.
Through the black fir-forest
Thunder harsh and dry,
Shattering down the snowflakes
Off the curdled sky.
Hark! The brave Northeaster!
Breast-high lies the scent,
On by holt and headland,
Over heath and bent.
Chime, ye dappled darlings,
Through the sleet and snow.

Who can override you?
Let the horses go!
Chime, ye dappled darlings,
Down the roaring blast;
You shall see a fox die
Ere an hour be past.
Go! and rest tomorrow,
Hunting in your dreams,
While our skates are ringing
O'er the frozen streams.
Let the luscious Southwind
Breathe in lovers' sighs,
While the lazy gallants
Bask in ladies' eyes.
What does he but soften
Heart alike and pen?
'Tis the hard gray weather
Breeds hard English men.
What's the soft Southwester?
'Tis the ladies' breeze,
Bringing home their trueloves
Out of all the seas.
But the black Northeaster,
Through the snowstorm hurled,
Drives our English hearts of oak
Seaward round the world.
Come, as came our fathers,
Heralded by thee,
Conquering from the eastward,
Lords by land and sea.
Come; and strong, within us
Stir the Viking's blood;
Bracing brain and sinew;
Blow, thou wind of God!

Greyfriars Bobby

In the early 1800s, a man named John Gray settled in Edinburgh, Scotland, with his wife and son. He was by trade a gardener, but because of the cold weather and hard ground, he took what work he could find, and so he became a constable, or what the common folk called a "bobby."

As part of his job, Mr. Gray was required to have a dog. The dog would not only be a friend and companion, but a valuable partner on nightly rounds he would make around his precinct. And so, he bought a Skye Terrier, and he named him Bobby.

Sadly, John Gray died not many years later of tuberculosis in 1858. He was buried in a churchyard called Greyfriars Kirkyard. For the next fourteen years, Bobby visited the churchyard every day and sat guard over his master's grave. He left only for food, which he got at a cafe he and John used to visit together. Although the keeper of the graveyard tried to keep Bobby out, it was no use, and he finally gave up and built a shelter for the dog instead.

Bobby became famous throughout the city, and crowds would daily come to see him leave for his meal at one o'clock. The people and governors of Edinburgh looked after Bobby until his death in 1872. In 1873 a statue of the faithful dog was erected on a street corner just opposite the churchyard. Bobby was buried near his master, and a line of his headstone reads: "Greyfriars Bobby - Let his loyalty and devotion be a lesson to us all."

Tea Time

Tea was not regularly sold in England until the 17th century. In 1657, a coffee house owned by merchant Thomas Garway started selling both liquid and dry tea to the public. It quickly became popular, and by 1750, over 500 coffee houses sold it. By that time, tea had become the favorite drink of Britain's lower classes. The British government decided to "cash in" on the people's preference for tea by taxing tea sales, but it soon became absurd. By 1850, the government was taxing 119% on the price of tea. In other words, the tax added onto a tea purchase would be a little more than twice the actual value of the tea! (Today, a normal sales tax on purchases is around 6%.) Because of this outrageous taxation, smugglers would buy tea illegally from foreign merchants and sell it for a much cheaper price. Finally, William Pitt, a wise and honored prime minister, reduced the tax to 12% and so ended smuggling and high taxation.

There are two customary tea times in England. The first is called *afternoon tea*. This is actually a small meal, in which tea (or coffee) is served with either freshly baked scones spread with cream and jam (cream tea), thickly sliced cucumber sandwiches with the crusts cut off, or assorted pastries. Afternoon tea became popular with the wealthy class in the 1850s, but it was never too common among the poorer classes, since they were out laboring at the time it was taken—four o'clock.

The second tea is called *high tea*. This was the meal traditionally eaten around six o'clock, the time that the working classes would be home from their jobs. High tea included tea with sweet foods, such as scones, breads, cakes, buns, and savory dishes like cheese on toast, toasted crumpets, cold meats and pickles, or poached eggs on toast.

Today, afternoon tea and high tea are not as common as they used to be. Although afternoon tea is still served in tea rooms, most people are working during this time. High tea is now replaced with a more substantial meal, called *dinner* or *supper*, because most folks eat their main meal at this time instead of midday, as the working classes once did.

There are many kinds of tea a person can buy, and they come from several different countries. For instance, many black teas come from India, while many green teas come from China and Japan. While there is a variety of tea, there is one way to make a perfect brew. Follow the directions below to make a perfect "cuppa" tea, and use the recommended brewing times, depending on what kind of tea you have.

Brewing Instructions

1. Store tea in an air-tight container at room temperature.
2. Always use freshly drawn boiling water.
3. Use one tea bag or one rounded teaspoon of loose tea for each cup served.
4. Allow the tea to brew for the recommended time before pouring.
5. If you brew tea from a bag and are using a mug, put any cream in last.

Recommended Brewing Times

Name	Country	Type	Time	Milk?
Gunpower	China	Green	3-4 min.	no
Jasmine	China	Green	2-3 min.	no
Oolong	China or Taiwan	Oolong	5-7 min.	no
Sencha	Japan	Green	2-2.5 min.	no
Darjeeling	India	Black	2-3 min.	no
Ceylon	Sri Lanka	Black	3-4 min.	yes or no
Kenya	Kenya	Black	3-4 min.	yes